The management of asbestos in non-domestic premises

Regulation 4 of the Control of Asbestos Regulations 2006

Approved Code of Practice and guidance

HSE Books

This Code has been approved by the Health and Safety Commission, with the consent of the Secretary of State. It gives practical advice on how to comply with the law. If you follow the advice you will be doing enough to comply with the law in respect of those specific matters on which the Code gives advice. You may use alternative methods to those set out in the Code in order to comply with the law.

However, the Code has a special legal status. If you are prosecuted for breach of health and safety law, and it is proved that you did not follow the relevant provisions of the Code, you will need to show that you have complied with the law in some other way or a Court will find you at fault.

Contents

Notice of Approval

By virtue of section 16(4) of the Health and Safety at Work etc. Act 1974 and with the consent of the Secretary of State for Work and Pensions, the Health and Safety Commission has on 25 July 2006 approved the Code of Practice entitled *The management of asbestos in non-domestic premises.*

The Code of Practice comes into effect on 13 November 2006.

The Code of Practice provides practical guidance on regulation 4 of the Control of Asbestos Regulations 2006. In particular it applies to those who have responsibilities for the maintenance and repair of non-domestic premises where asbestos-containing materials are or are likely to be present in those premises.

The Code of Practice re-issues, substantively unchanged, the guidance contained in an earlier Code of Practice (L127 First edition) which ceased to have effect on 13 November 2006, being the date on which the Control of Asbestos Regulations 2006 came into force.

Signed

SUSAN MAWER
Secretary to the Health and Safety Commission

20 October 2006

Introduction

The status of Approved Codes of Practice

1   This document provides advice on how to comply with regulation 4 of the Control of Asbestos Regulations 2006 (the Asbestos Regulations). It contains an Approved Code of Practice (ACOP), which gives advice on the preferred means of compliance with the regulation. This advice has a special legal status – if you are prosecuted for a breach of health and safety law and it is proved that you did not follow the relevant provisions of an ACOP, you will need to show that you have complied with the law in some other way or a court will find you at fault. The document also contains more general guidance on ways to comply with the law, which does not have this special status. The ACOP is in bold type and the more general guidance material is in normal type.

Scope

2   This ACOP provides advice on the duties under regulation 4 of the Asbestos Regulations to manage the risk from asbestos in non-domestic premises. It explains the duties of building owners, tenants and any other parties who have any legal responsibility for the premises. It also sets out what is required of people who have a duty to co-operate with the main dutyholder to enable them to comply with the regulation.

3   Regulation 4 requires dutyholders to:

(a)   take reasonable steps to find materials in premises likely to contain asbestos and to check their condition;

(b)   presume that materials contain asbestos unless there is strong evidence to suppose they do not;

(c)   make a written record of the location and condition of asbestos and presumed asbestos-containing materials (ACMs) and keep the record up to date;

(d)   assess the risk of the likelihood of anyone being exposed to these materials; and

(e)   prepare a plan to manage that risk and put it into effect to ensure that:

(i)   any material known or presumed to contain asbestos is kept in a good state of repair;

(ii)   any material that contains or is presumed to contain asbestos is, because of the risks associated with its location or condition, repaired or if necessary removed; and

(iii)   information on the location and condition of the material is given to anyone potentially at risk.

4   This ACOP and guidance give advice on ways to manage the risk from asbestos in non-domestic premises. The aim is to protect workers who may come across asbestos in the course of their day-to-day activities. However, this should also result in the protection of any other people who may be at risk from the potential release of asbestos fibres into the air. The ACOP takes you step by step through the requirements of regulation 4.

5   This ACOP will also be useful to anyone who is in charge of maintenance work undertaken either by contractors or by directly employed workers. This might be the sole proprietor of a small business or the estate manager or health and safety manager of a large one. Safety representatives may also find the information valuable. Safety representatives are entitled to have access to a copy of the ACOP and guidance held by their employers. To comply with the duties held under the Safety Representatives and Safety Committee Regulations 1977, employers should provide access to a copy of the ACOP and guidance to safety representatives. Employers should also offer technical assistance should the safety representatives not understand what the requirements mean.

6   There is one other ACOP giving advice on the Asbestos Regulations. The ACOP, *Work with materials containing asbestos. Control of Asbestos Regulations 2006. Approved Code of Practice and guidance*[1] applies to all work with asbestos, in particular to work on or which disturbs building materials containing asbestos, asbestos sampling and laboratory analysis. It will also help people who commission these types of work.

Domestic rented premises

7   The duty to manage asbestos in premises does apply to common parts of premises, including housing developments and blocks of flats, but does not place any direct duties on landlords in respect of individual houses or flats. However, landlords do have to meet the requirements of the Defective Premises Act 1972 in England and Wales or the Civic Government (Scotland) Act 1982 in Scotland. A domestic premises is a private dwelling in which a person lives. Legal precedents have established that common parts of flats are not part of the private dwelling and are therefore classified as non-domestic. This would include the common parts of both purpose-built blocks of flats and in some cases conversions to flats. Examples of common parts would include foyers, corridors, lifts and lift shafts, staircases, boilerhouses, vertical risers, gardens, yards and outhouses. However it would not apply to rooms within a private residence that are shared by more than one household such as bathrooms, kitchens etc in shared houses and communal dining rooms and lounges in sheltered accommodation.

Background

What is asbestos and where might you find it?

8   Asbestos is a naturally occurring mineral. It can be amphibole asbestos which includes crocidolite (blue) and amosite (brown) asbestos, or serpentine asbestos which is chrysotile (white) asbestos. These are the three main types used in Great Britain.

9   Exposure to amphibole asbestos poses a greater health hazard than exposure to chrysotile, but all types can cause asbestos-related diseases.

10   Asbestos-containing products have been widely used in buildings as construction materials, fireproofing, thermal insulation, electrical insulation, sound insulation, decorative plasters, roofing products, flooring products, heat-resistant materials, gaskets, friction products etc. Further information is available in HSE's guidance on the management of asbestos in premises.[2] In the 1960s and 1970s annual imports of asbestos-containing products peaked at over 150 000 tonnes each year. Since 1985 the new use of any material containing blue and brown asbestos has been banned. This means that in Britain there are many thousands of tonnes of asbestos still in buildings, where, so long as it is in good condition and remains undisturbed, it does not present a risk.

11   By 1999 the new use of any building materials containing white asbestos had been banned. Therefore, an assessment of premises constructed after 1999 should be very easy. Unless you have information to the contrary, you would simply have to record the fact that the date of construction indicates there is no asbestos present.

Why is it a problem?

12   When asbestos is disturbed or damaged, the fibres are released into the air and people breathe them in, which creates a risk to human health. The types of work that release fibres include, for example, drilling holes with power tools, sawing or sanding material. Simply working near to material containing asbestos might result in disturbance, particularly if it is in poor condition. Accidental damage, wear and tear or vandalism can release fibres from the ACMs, for example in walls, ceilings and floor coverings.

13   We know that all forms of asbestos may cause asbestosis, lung cancer or mesothelioma. Therefore, where exposure to asbestos cannot be prevented entirely, exposures need to be controlled as far as is reasonably practicable.

14   As mentioned in paragraphs 10 and 11, new use of asbestos in buildings is now illegal. However, ACMs are still present in many buildings where people can cut, sand or drill into them or near them without being aware of what they are.

15   In 1995 Professor Julian Peto, HSE epidemiologists and other researchers published an influential scientific paper[3] which identified the largest group of workers at risk from asbestos exposure. These were building workers, particularly those involved in demolition, maintenance, repair and refurbishment, and workers such as plumbers, electricians, joiners, computer and telecommunication engineers – people who may encounter asbestos during their normal day-to-day work.

16   The paper indicates that a quarter of those now dying from asbestos-related diseases worked in the building trades at some time in their lives. Although the future death rate will be largely due to the legacy from exposures to asbestos which took place between 15 and 60 years ago, when the use of asbestos was widespread and work with it was not as strictly controlled as it is today, building maintenance and repair workers are still at risk of exposure when carrying out work on buildings which contain asbestos. It should also be remembered that those who occupy the building can also be at risk, if the materials are disturbed to release asbestos fibres.

17   Employers of building maintenance and repair workers are required to carry out a risk assessment before undertaking any work which exposes, or is liable to expose, employees to asbestos. They must then take the appropriate steps required by the Asbestos Regulations to prevent or reduce these risks. However, in many cases, the employers and their workers have little or no information about the premises where they are going to undertake work, and are not aware if ACMs are present. Consequently, it is difficult for them to consider the risks, or if precautions may be needed. A duty to manage the risk from asbestos in non-domestic premises was therefore added to the Control of Asbestos at Work Regulations 2002 to address this. These requirements have since been brought forward unchanged in the Control of Asbestos Regulations 2006.

Legal duties in addition to the duty to manage asbestos

18   The duties imposed by regulation 4 of the Asbestos Regulations supplement the provisions of the Health and Safety at Work etc Act 1974[4] (the HSW Act) and some of the duties imposed by other sets of regulations:

(a)   the HSW Act requires employers to conduct their work in such a way that their employees will not be exposed to health and safety risks, and to provide information to other people about their workplace which might affect their health and safety. Section 3 of the HSW Act contains general duties on employers and the self-employed in respect of people other than their own employees. Section 4 contains general duties for anyone who has control, to any extent, over a workplace;

(b)   the Management of Health and Safety at Work Regulations 1999[5] (the Management Regulations) which require employers and self-employed people to make an assessment of the risks to the health and safety of themselves, employees and people not in their employment, arising out of or in connection with the conduct of their business – and to make appropriate arrangements for protecting those people's health and safety. Any assessment made for the purposes of the Asbestos Regulations will not need to be repeated for the Management Regulations;

(c)   the Workplace (Health, Safety and Welfare) Regulations 1992[6] which require employers to maintain workplace buildings so as to protect occupants and workers;

(d)   the Construction (Design and Management) Regulations 1994[7] (CDM) which require the client to pass on information about the state or condition of any premises (including the presence of hazardous materials such as asbestos) to the planning supervisor before any work begins and to ensure that the health and safety file is available for inspection by any person who needs the information;

(e)   the Defective Premises Act 1972 in England and Wales or the Civic Government (Scotland) Act 1982 in Scotland place duties on landlords to take reasonable care to see that tenants and other people are safe from personal injury or disease caused by a defect in the state of the premises. Any premises in such a state as to be prejudicial to health constitute a statutory nuisance under section 79 of the Environmental Protection Act 1990. An abatement notice can be served by local authorities on the owner or occupier of premises requiring prevention or restriction of the nuisance;

(f)   as well as imposing a duty to manage asbestos in premises, the Asbestos Regulations require employers to:

(i)   undertake risk assessments before commencing work which exposes, or is liable to expose, employees to asbestos;

(ii)   produce a plan of work detailing how the work is to be carried out; and

(iii)   either prevent exposure to asbestos or reduce it to as low a level as is reasonably practicable.

19   A range of other legislative requirements is also included, for example on the use and maintenance of control measures and protective clothing, and a duty to prevent the spread of asbestos.

20   The regulation 4 duty complements the above duties and makes general legal duties specific, to ensure that all the risks from asbestos are properly addressed.

Who has a duty to manage asbestos?

21   A wide range of people potentially have obligations under this regulation, including employers and the self-employed, if they have responsibilities for maintaining or repairing non-domestic premises, and the owner of those premises, whether they are occupied or vacant. In all these cases, regulation 4 of the Asbestos Regulations may apply, but the extent of the practical duties will be determined by contractual and other existing legal obligations towards the property. This is explored in more detail in later paragraphs.

Regulation 4

Duties of owners, occupiers, managing agents and others

Regulation

4(1)

(1)   In this regulation "the dutyholder" means –

(a)   every person who has, by virtue of a contract or tenancy, an obligation of any extent in relation to the maintenance or repair of non-domestic premises or any means of access thereto or egress therefrom; or

(b)   in relation to any part of non-domestic premises where there is no such contract or tenancy, every person who has, to any extent, control of that part of those non-domestic premises or any means of access thereto or egress therefrom,

and where there is more than one such dutyholder, the relative contribution to be made by each such person in complying with the requirements of this regulation will be determined by the nature and extent of the maintenance and repair obligation owed by that person.

ACOP

22   The duties in regulation 4 rest with the person in control of maintenance activities in the non-domestic premises, whether that be the occupier or landlord, sub-lessor or managing agent. Where no such obligation exists, eg where there is no tenancy agreement or contract, or where the premises are unoccupied, then regulation 4(1)(b) places the duty on the person in control of the premises to comply with this regulation.

23   The extent of this duty will therefore in most cases be determined by the degree of responsibility over matters concerning the fabric of the building and maintenance activities carried out there. An owner may rent or lease out workplace premises under agreements where the tenants are responsible for all alterations, maintenance and repairs in the premises. But if the premises are non-domestic and the owner is responsible for maintenance and repairs and controls access by maintenance workers into the building, the owner must carry out the work required by regulation 4 themselves. In that situation, the owner's obligations will extend to:

(a)   carrying out an assessment as to whether asbestos is present and determining its condition;

(b)   recording the results of the assessment and ensuring that they are passed on to the occupier of the premises;

(c)   collaborating with the occupier and others in the preparation and implementation of the management plan to control the risk from the ACM; and

(d)   ensuring that anyone potentially at risk receives information on the location and condition of the material, so far as it is within their control.

24   Where sole responsibility rests with the owner, for example in the common parts of multi-occupied buildings, or where there is no tenancy agreement or contract, eg the premises are unoccupied or occupied solely by the owner, they would have the duty for complying with regulation 4 for those premises or parts of premises.

4(1)

Guidance

4(1)

25   The detail of any contracts/tenancy agreements should be referred to when trying to determine who is responsible for which aspects of the requirements. Examples of some of the tenancy arrangements and how responsibilities may be shared under the regulation are set out in paragraphs 26-35.

Example 1: Shared responsibilities between the owner and occupier of the premises

26 The owner or leaseholder may retain control of the walls, roof and common parts of the premises, but the employer in occupation may be responsible for the internal parts of the premises they occupy. The employer would have to identify all accessible ACMs and assess their condition in the parts of the premises for which they are responsible, or presume that materials they could not identify contain asbestos. The owner should make all relevant information on these parts of the premises available to the employer. The owner would have to carry out these actions for the rest of the premises. However the owner may choose to undertake the identification themselves for the entire building and then provide the employer in occupation with that information.

27 The employer in occupation and the owner would need to prepare and implement a plan to manage the risk from the ACMs for which they are responsible. In practice it would be more appropriate for one plan to be jointly prepared and implemented by the owner and employer in occupation. Both would have to carry out any actions needed to manage the risk from the ACMs, including where necessary any repairs or removal of these materials. Again, it may be more appropriate for joint action or for one party to arrange for all the work in agreement with the other.

28 The employer in occupation must ensure that information on the location and condition of all ACMs is given to anyone liable to disturb the material. Where the owner commissions repairs or maintenance work they must ensure that the person or organisation they employ is provided with this information.

Example 2: The owner/leaseholder retains all responsibilities for the premises

29 The owner may retain all responsibilities for the repair and maintenance of the premises, eg for the fabric of the building itself or arranging for maintenance work to be done. In this case, the owner must identify ACMs for the entire premises and assess their condition, or presume that the materials they cannot identify contain asbestos. They must then assess the risk from the material and prepare the plan to manage the asbestos. The owner would need to inform the employers in occupation how the plan is to be implemented and, in particular, how arrangements are made to inform those potentially at risk from the disturbance of the ACMs. It may be that the employers in occupation will need this information so that they can tell anyone coming to the premises of the whereabouts of the ACMs.

Example 3: The employer in occupation takes on all the responsibilities

30 The employer in occupation would have to carry out or arrange to carry out an assessment of each building under their control. They would then have to complete a risk assessment and prepare an action plan for the premises. A record of the asbestos present, such as a register, must be compiled and kept up to date by the occupier. The employer in occupation should also ensure that the owner/leaseholder or other interested parties are given access to the information.

Example 4: Responsibilities for the premises are shared between many parties

31 There may be an owner, several sub-lessors, and employers in occupation who retain different responsibilities. In addition to the duty of co-operation in regulation 4 (see paragraph 35), the employers in occupation of the premises have a general duty of co-operation to comply with the requirements of any health and

safety regulations under regulation 11 of the Management Regulations. They would therefore have jointly to carry out the actions required to comply with regulation 4 of the Asbestos Regulations for those parts of the premises for which they have maintenance and repair responsibilities. Each other party (eg owner, managing agent) would have to provide all relevant information on the premises to the employers. The employers in occupation would have to co-operate in the development and implementation of the plan to manage the risk as far as their responsibilities dictate. The owner, managing agent, or lessor would have to carry out these actions for those parts of the premises for which they retain maintenance and repair responsibilities. Where any party can authorise any repairs or maintenance of the premises they should pass information on the ACMs to those who are likely to disturb the material.

32   It will be for each party to decide how they are going to comply with the regulation but it may be more practical for one party to take the lead in carrying out the action required in co-operation with the others. This could be the owner, managing agent or the employer who occupies the largest part of the premises. But each party must ensure that their duties under regulation 4 are carried out. Responsibility for the costs of complying with the duty will need to be considered by all parties, based on the contractual agreements between each of them and legal requirements they each have.

Example 5: Managing agent

33   The owner/leaseholder may pass all or some responsibilities for maintenance and repair of the premises to a managing agent. The agent would be required to carry out the actions in the same ways as the owner. However, this does not necessarily mean that the owner has passed on his legal obligations to comply with the 'duty to manage' regulation.

Changes in tenancy/occupation

34   If the terms of the tenancy are altered substantially, or if the building is vacated, the owner or leaseholder must ensure that all relevant information is passed to any new occupier (see regulation 4(9)(c)(i)).

4(1)

Regulation 4(2)

(2)   Every person shall cooperate with the dutyholder so far as is necessary to enable the dutyholder to comply with his duties under this regulation.

Guidance

35   Other people who are not dutyholders, but have information on or control of the premises, are required to assist the dutyholders, as far as is necessary, to comply with the duty. However this co-operation does not extend to paying for or sharing the costs of any actions the dutyholder takes to manage these risks. An owner who has no maintenance and repair responsibilities for the premises will still need to provide any information they have on the building which will help to confirm if ACMs are present. Architects, surveyors or building contractors who were involved in the construction or maintenance of the building may also have such information and would be expected to make this available at a justifiable and reasonable cost. Those in occupation of the premises, who have no maintenance or repair responsibilities, may still control access to the premises. They will be required to co-operate in allowing the dutyholder access to carry out the actions necessary to comply with the duty. They may also need to provide information (that has been stored on site) on the location and condition of the material to maintenance workers coming to the premises, so that they do not unknowingly disturb asbestos.

4(2)

What has to be done and how

36   There are five stages to this, detailed in Parts A to E (paragraphs 37-111).

A   Delegating the task

37   Although the ACOP refers to dutyholder, someone else can be nominated to do all or part of the work – but note that the legal responsibility cannot be delegated. Anyone who is asked to do some work as a result of this regulation must know what it is they have to do and be able to do it safely. They should have suitable competence and training for this work. Employees and safety representatives must be consulted in good time about the appointment of any competent person.

38   If the dutyholder decides to appoint a separate organisation or person to carry out some or all of this work, they should assess whether the individual or organisation concerned:

(a)   have adequate training and experience in such work;

(b)   can demonstrate independence, impartiality and integrity;

(c)   have an adequate quality management system;

(d)   are carrying out any survey in accordance with recommended guidance, MDHS100 *Surveying, sampling and assessment of asbestos-containing materials*.[8]

4(2)

39   If a dutyholder chooses to appoint a third party to carry out a survey, they can assess if they are likely to have adequate experience and training by checking whether the organisation is accredited by a recognised accreditation body as complying with BS EN ISO 17020[9] to undertake surveys for ACMs. Alternatively, they can check if the individual surveyor has personnel certification for asbestos surveys from a certification body, which has been accredited by a recognised accreditation body under BS EN ISO/IEC 17024.[10] The United Kingdom Accreditation Service (UKAS) is currently the sole recognised accreditation body in Great Britain. The technical guidance MDHS100[8] specifies three types of survey, each requiring a different level of competence. Before employing anyone to undertake a survey, you are strongly advised to check that the person you employ has the relevant accreditation for the type of survey you request and practical experience of the type of building.

40   There are differences between accreditation and personnel certification schemes, although both provide measures of competence. Accreditation provides assurance that an organisation employs competent individuals and also that there is a framework or quality system within which those individuals are required to work. Personnel certification provides assurance that an individual has demonstrated a defined level of competence to carry out specific activities, but does not look at the infrastructure within which they work.

41   If personnel are being employed to identify ACMs through sampling and analysis, accreditation by UKAS, under either BS EN ISO 17025[11] or BS EN ISO 17020[9] as appropriate, would indicate that they are likely to be competent.

42   A third party may be employed to act as a consultant or project manager for the work needed to meet the requirements of regulation 4, but again the employer should make sure that they are sufficiently competent. The Management

4(2)

Guidance

4(2)

Regulations say that a person shall be regarded as competent 'where he has sufficient training and experience or knowledge and other qualities to enable him properly to assist in undertaking the measures referred to'.

ACOP

4(2)

43   The person with the duties under regulation 4 (whether they are the employer, self-employed person who is in charge of the workplace, or owner) should make sure that everyone who works in the premises knows who has been nominated and what tasks they have been given. This information should be disseminated to all employees whenever possible.

B   Finding ACMs and assessing their condition

Regulation

4(3), (4) and (5)

(3)   In order to enable him to manage the risk from asbestos in non-domestic premises, the dutyholder shall ensure that a suitable and sufficient assessment is carried out as to whether asbestos is or is liable to be present in the premises.

(4)   In making the assessment –

(a)   such steps as are reasonable in the circumstances shall be taken; and

(b)   the condition of any asbestos which is, or has been assumed to be, present in the premises shall be considered.

(5)   Without prejudice to the generality of paragraph (4), the dutyholder shall ensure that –

(a)   account is taken of building plans or other relevant information and of the age of the premises; and

(b)   an inspection is made of those parts of the premises which are reasonably accessible.

ACOP

4(3), (4) and (5)

44   To comply with this part of the duty, an assessment will have to be made as to whether or not there is or may be any asbestos anywhere in the premises and its condition checked. Warehouses, yards, sheds, outbuildings, under-floor service ducts, corridors, vertical risers, external runs of pipes and bridges should all be included – in fact any part of the premises where asbestos might have been used. Fixed plant and machinery, like printing machines and parts of process plant and also mobile units which are on the premises all the time, must be included, but not those which only come onto the premises from time to time, such as heavy trucks which might have asbestos brake linings. (The Road Vehicles (Brake Linings Safety) Regulations 1999 (as amended) apply to those.)

Guidance

4(3), (4) and (5)

45   Detailed guidance on what to look for and how to go about the inspection is available in MDHS100.[8]

ACOP

4(3), (4) and (5)

46   Everything that can reasonably be done must be done to decide whether there is (or may be) asbestos in the premises, and if there is some (or may be some), to find out where it is or is likely to be. The condition of the material must also be checked.

ACOP

4(3), (4) and (5)

47 As much information as practicable will need to be found out about the buildings and plant in the premises. The regulation requires that all documentary information that can be obtained about the premises is gone through systematically and then a thorough inspection of the premises themselves is carried out, both inside and outside. When this has been done, anyone who may be able to provide more information should be consulted – including architects, building surveyors, building contractors, safety representatives and members of staff who are familiar with the premises. Any information that has been provided must be checked for accuracy.

Guidance

4(3), (4) and (5)

48 The Safety Representatives and Safety Committees Regulations 1977[12] give safety representatives the right to be consulted on matters affecting the group or groups of employees they represent. They also have the right (on reasonable notice being given) to inspect and take copies of any document relevant to the workplace or to the employees represented, which the employer is required to keep by virtue of any relevant statutory provision. This means they should be consulted about the assessment and they have the right to see any records made in connection with this work.

49 Broadly similar rights and duties are conferred with regard to employees not represented by trade union safety representatives – by the Health and Safety (Consultation with Employees) Regulations 1996,[13] in that an employer is obliged to consult employees on the introduction of any measure at the workplace which may substantially affect the health and safety of those employees (such as the asbestos management plan) and is obliged to provide them with the information they need so that they can participate fully in the consultation.

ACOP

4(3), (4) and (5)

50 During the inspection of the premises, if any material is found that looks as though it might contain asbestos, it should be presumed that it does, unless there already is strong evidence that it does not. (Examples of the sort of evidence might be: the result of a sample having been tested; information from the manufacturer; or information collected during the documentary search.) Enough information about any material that it is thought might contain asbestos should be noted on a record or drawing to enable another person to identify it. The record or drawing will need to include where it is located, the extent of the ACM, what condition it is in and what form it is in (eg the product type – tiles, boards, cement sheets), and what it looks like (eg if it is painted, what colour). This information will help you to assess the risks from the material (see paragraphs 65-81).

Guidance

4(3), (4) and (5)

51 The first thing to do is to gather together and consider all the information that can be obtained about the premises, such as:

(a) the age of the building;

(b) any plans and specifications that may exist or can be obtained;

(c) details about whether the building has ever been extended, adapted or refurbished, and if it has, when the work was done;

(d) information that may have been given by builders or installation engineers. For example, building drawings that clearly show what materials were used during construction/reconstruction. Original builders' invoices, if these are sufficiently detailed, may also have this information.

52 You should take into account existing surveys/assessments of the premises, but you would need to consider how accurate they are. This would be based on when they were done, whether they are up to date, what parts of the premises they covered and if they comply with current requirements in this ACOP.

Guidance

53 An accurate drawing of the premises should be obtained or made, and the main features of each room and passageway marked on it. Any information (such as room and floor numbers) should be marked as this will help the identification of individual locations. Where there are only a few ACMs in the premises the drawing may not have to be very detailed and only cover the rooms in which they are present. However, more complex premises may need to use building plans on which each ACM can be accurately marked to show the location and extent of the material.

54 The drawing might be used to record the information collected about the premises and what is found when the inspection of the premises is made. Whatever means is used to record information, others must easily be able to identify the places where it is suspected there may be asbestos. You may find with more complex premises that taking photographs will be a useful way of doing this.

55 When the documents are looked through, if evidence is found that asbestos was used when the premises were built or during any refurbishment, repair or installation which was done later, the details should be recorded on the drawing – noting where it is and if possible, what form it is in and what it is used for.

56 For the inspection of the premises, every part of the premises will need to be thoroughly searched (eg every room, corridor and access way, all external pipework etc). The findings will need to be recorded clearly. In places where access is only reasonable at certain times (for example, during the maintenance of fixed plant or during refurbishment of a building) arrangements should be made for the inspection of those areas to take place then, and the information noted in the records when it has been done. Bear in mind that some areas of the premises may contain hidden material that contains asbestos, for example within walls, roof voids, and fire doors. These areas would need to be taken into account during maintenance activities or if demolition of the premises is proposed.

4(3), (4) and (5)

ACOP
4(3), (4) and (5)

57 You will need to record on the drawing any area not accessed or inspected and it must be assumed to contain asbestos unless you have strong evidence that it does not.

Guidance

58 Before beginning, consider other hazards such as heights, fragility of roofs, confined spaces etc. Ensure that the proper precautions are taken. If possible, do the work with a partner who knows the premises well. If asbestos is present, regulations 6 and 10 of the Asbestos Regulations will need to be complied with, by assessing the risk of exposure to employees and if necessary taking measures to prevent that risk.

59 Use the inspection to check that the documentary evidence collected is accurate. Sometimes asbestos was used in a building even though a more expensive material had been specified on the plans. Also, there may be information that asbestos has been removed from the premises in earlier years, but this may not have been carried out to a standard that would be acceptable today. For example, certain materials may have been missed.

60 Some materials obviously do not contain asbestos, for example, solid wood and glass, ordinary bricks and stone such as sandstone and York stone. Some materials, such as cement rain gutters and downpipes, almost always contain asbestos. An example of a type of material where it is difficult to be sure about asbestos content are the boards used to make items like wall panels and ceiling tiles. These can be difficult to identify, especially if they are painted or wallpapered. Insulation of any sort is also difficult to identify, except foam and polystyrene. Partition wall boards, ceiling tiles, and insulation materials on

4(3), (4) and (5)

Guidance

4(3), (4) and (5)

pipework and boilers need to be treated as though they contain asbestos, unless there is strong evidence that they do not. But if it is known that a partition wall is made of plasterboard, eg because someone remembers when it was built, or it is known that some materials have been removed, this can be noted on the drawing.

61   Once a material has been identified or presumed to contain asbestos, you must check the condition and also note this on your drawing. Further advice is available both from the guidance on asbestos surveys MDHS100[8] and on the management of asbestos in premises.[2]

ACOP

4(3), (4) and (5)

62   If the inspection provides strong evidence to believe that there is no asbestos in the premises, nothing else needs to be done about this regulation, except to note the work already done, in case an inspector needs to see it. But the assessment must be reviewed if any new information is received that leads to the suspicion that there may, after all, be some asbestos on the premises.

Regulation

4(6) and (7)

(6)   The dutyholder shall ensure that the assessment is reviewed forthwith if –

(a)   there is reason to suspect that the assessment is no longer valid; or

(b)   there has been a significant change in the premises to which the assessment relates.

(7)   The dutyholder shall ensure that the conclusions of the assessment and every review are recorded.

ACOP

4(6) and (7)

63   Unless there is strong evidence that there is no asbestos in the premises, the drawing/record must be reviewed and brought up to date every time it is known that something has changed that affects the risks from the material. For example, if some building work is done, some of the asbestos material is removed, or if someone else (like a heating or installation engineer) provides some more information about where asbestos may be, and whether the material is damaged. The drawing/record should be available on site for the entire life of the premises and must be kept up to date, as far as is reasonably practicable. This can be a paper copy of the drawing/record or a copy that is accessible from a computer database.

Guidance
4(6) and (7)

64   If asbestos is, or is liable to be, on the premises, the next step is to decide how the risk from it will be assessed and managed.

C   Assessing the risk

Regulation

4(8)

(8)   Where the assessment shows that asbestos is or is liable to be present in any part of the premises the dutyholder shall ensure that –

(a)   a determination of the risk from that asbestos is made;

ACOP

4(8)

65   As part of the assessment of the risk of anyone being exposed to asbestos from any ACM identified, the information on the drawing or record of location of the materials and their condition, which was made as part of the inspection, should be used. Then, it must be decided what is going to be done to make sure that the identified risks from the materials are managed to prevent people from being exposed to asbestos, so far as is reasonably practicable.

Guidance
4(8)

66   When the documentary research and the inspection of the premises have been completed, there should be a drawing of the site, or some other record (eg the

report of any survey commissioned), with the locations and descriptions of any possible ACMs noted on it. (Assume that these materials all contain asbestos, unless there is proof that they do not, eg results of sampling.) This information needs to be used to help assess the risk from the materials and then to go on to decide how those risks are to be managed. Further guidance on the risks from specific asbestos material is in Table 1 of MDHS100[8] and general asbestos risk management guidance is available.[2]

67 Consider how likely it is that each area of ACM will be disturbed or damaged by maintenance, repair or refurbishment and by other activities.

68 Remember, for asbestos to pose a risk, asbestos fibres must be released from the ACM and become airborne. (Some asbestos might not be very likely to cause harm, eg asbestos cement in good condition does not easily release fibres.) Think about the material itself, where it is located and what types of maintenance or other disturbances are likely to take place.

69 Materials which:

(a) have already deteriorated or been damaged;

(b) are likely to be disturbed in the course of planned work, eg require regular repair or maintenance;

(c) are very accessible and likely to be disturbed or damaged in normal use;

(d) may be damaged by vandalism;

will present a greater risk. Each separate location and type of material will need to be assessed individually. It can then be worked out which of these is most likely to be disturbed and release high concentrations of airborne fibres. This will help to provide some of the information needed to decide what to do and which material should have the highest priority for action (eg repair, sealing, removal or leaving in place and monitoring the condition).

70 The most significant risk will be from asbestos in areas where maintenance or reorganisation is needed regularly, particularly if those areas are subject to heavy use during the normal working day. Or, where there is asbestos which is liable to damage (for example where it might be hit by fork-lift trucks or heavy trolleys or maintenance of air-conditioning and heating systems will disturb it). The risk will be greater still if the material is in a confined space and/or an unventilated area. Remember that the potential for disturbance must be considered. For example a maintenance worker using power tools close to a material containing asbestos could disturb it.

71 There is unlikely to be any significant risk from ACMs in areas which are unoccupied, inaccessible, and not likely to be disturbed by maintenance activities.

72 If ACMs are suitably identified, eg labelled or colour coded, and the room they are in is locked so that no one can get in without permission, there will not be much risk that a person will unknowingly work on them without having proper protection. If ACMs are not identified and they are in an area where people are likely to do maintenance, there will be a high risk of someone working on them, or accidentally damaging them without knowing that they contain asbestos.

73 Even where ACMs are in parts of the premises where people work regularly they will not present a high risk to health, provided that: the material is in good

Guidance

4(8)

condition and fibres cannot escape into the air; it is not prone to accidental damage or vandalism; and there is a system in place to prevent anyone from working on it without proper protection.

Condition of materials

74   The condition of ACMs can vary from completely undamaged (good condition) through to severely damaged (poor condition). Paragraphs 75-81 set out what are the appropriate actions to manage the risks from the material. The amount of damage and the potential for different types of materials to readily release fibres will ultimately determine the course of action that is appropriate to ensure no one is exposed to asbestos fibres. (Table 1 of MDHS100[8] gives information on the potential for materials to release fibres.)

Material in good condition

75   ACMs only have the potential to damage health if they release dust and fibres into the air which people breathe. This may happen because of accidental or deliberate damage or disturbance.

ACOP

4(8)

76   If the materials are in good condition and are unlikely to be damaged or disturbed, then it is better to leave them in place and to introduce a system of management.

Guidance

77   To decide whether a particular area of material is in good condition, ask the question, 'Are any fibres likely to be released from this?'. Remember that a visual inspection of the material and of the surrounding area needs to be undertaken to check if there may be deposits of material on any nearby surface.

78   If the material is intact, there is no need to remove or interfere with it in any way. Just make sure that it is noted in the records, and that no one interferes with it unless the proper precautions have been taken.

79   There are circumstances where ACMs will have to be removed, despite the fact that they are in good condition. For example, where demolition is planned or where major building work or maintenance is likely to disturb them, they should be removed before work starts. However, where removal of ACMs is time-consuming and resource-intensive and only involves a lower risk material such as textured decorative coatings containing asbestos, then removal before demolition or major refurbishment may not be reasonably practicable. Where ACMs are in places where they are very likely to be damaged, or where they are already badly damaged, management alone may not be enough. If it is asbestos coating or asbestos insulating board, consider calling in a specialist removal contractor (licensed by HSE) and having those materials removed.

4(8)

ACOP

Material in poor condition

80   ACMs in poor condition must be repaired or removed. Poor condition means that the material's exposed surface is in a state where there are substantial areas of visibly loose fibres that may be released by very slight disturbance or any material which has suffered significant damage or deterioration. (Examples of potential disturbance would be someone using high-speed power tools close by or the vibration of nearby plant or another form of contact with the material.)

4(8)

Guidance

4(8)

81   ACMs which are only slightly damaged can be repaired, encapsulated or enclosed. These options are worth considering if no major alterations or refurbishment to that area of the premises are planned. ACMs which are damaged

Guidance

4(8)

and cannot be repaired would usually need to be removed or sealed away. However there are some materials such as asbestos cement and floor tiles where fibres are firmly bound into the matrix of material. These materials are less likely to easily release fibres even when damaged. The separate guidance on the management of asbestos in premises[2] provides information on the different methods of making asbestos safe.

D   Managing the risk and preparing a plan

Regulation

4(8) and (9)

(8)   Where the assessment shows that asbestos is or is liable to be present in any part of the premises the dutyholder shall ensure that –

(b)   a written plan identifying those parts of the premises concerned is prepared; and

(c)   the measures which are to be taken for managing the risk are specified in the written plan.

(9)   The measures to be specified in the plan for managing the risk shall include adequate measures for –

(b)   ensuring any asbestos or any such substance is properly maintained or where necessary safely removed; and

Guidance
4(8) and (9)

82   A written plan needs to be prepared which sets out how the risks from any asbestos found during the search are to be managed. The plan can be a paper copy or a copy that is accessible from a computer database.

ACOP
4(8) and (9)

83   Managing the risk means making sure that as far as reasonably practicable no one can come to any harm from asbestos on the premises.

Guidance

84   The plan will need to specify whether any repair or removal work needs to be done, and the order of priority for this. Generally the areas of highest risk will need the earliest attention and the strictest management. A plan must be formulated that manages any asbestos that has been left in place, so that its potential danger is tightly controlled and the risks are kept to a minimum practical level. For other advice on these matters, see the separate guidance and leaflet on managing the risks from asbestos.[2,14]

85   When considering whether to remove or repair and manage, take as much information as possible into account, including the following:

(a)   What is the type of asbestos and what is the base material in which it is contained? The asbestos may be crocidolite, amosite or chrysotile (commonly known as blue, brown or white asbestos respectively, though colour is not an accurate guide to the type) or a mixture (see MDHS100[8] for more details).

(b)   What is the condition of the material now? If it is already crumbling or breaking away from the base, complete removal should be considered. For any minor surface damage, effective treatment suited to the material will need to be carried out. The HSE guidance Asbestos essentials[15,16] gives advice on minor work with asbestos. Asbestos essentials task sheets can also be found on HSE's website at www.hse.gov.uk/asbestos/essentials/index.htm.

(c)   Is the material in a place where it is likely to be damaged? For example, could it be damaged through bumping by fork-lift trucks, hospital trolleys etc, or deteriorate because of environmental factors, eg rain water? Employees may be able to provide information about this.

4(8) and (9)

Guidance

4(8) and (9)

(d) Is the material easy to get at or would major structural work be needed to allow its removal? Work out the cost of having the ACMs completely sealed away and balance that against the cost of removal. Also take into account the cost of closing off the area during repair or removal, reorganising normal activities and possible evacuation of the building while the work is going on. If some or all of the material is left where it is, note that it is there and make plans to manage the risk from it.

(e) If the asbestos is removed, what else will need to be done? For example, has asbestos insulation been provided for fire protection? If so, does it need to be replaced by other fire-resistant materials? If it does, consider what has to be done to satisfy the fire authority and insurers during the removal and replacement process. Further advice on the management and disposal of waste asbestos is given in the ACOP *Work with materials containing asbestos. Control of Asbestos Regulations 2006. Approved Code of Practice.*[1]

(f) The knowledge and experiences of the safety representatives and the workforce. Workers and safety representatives who know the premises are a valuable source of information.

86 Remember, if ACMs are in good condition and are unlikely to be damaged or disturbed, then it is better to leave them in place and to introduce a system of management.

ACOP

4(8) and (9)

87 Decisions about what to do to manage the risk from each area of ACM in the premises must be recorded and the records/drawings must be kept fully up to date. For example, if a decision has been made to remove ACMs, once this is done it should be reflected in the drawings/records. Access to a copy of the up-to-date drawings/records should be available on site for the entire life of the premises as far as is reasonably practicable (or if the premises are vacant, at the dutyholder's nearest occupied premises). The arrangements made to check that the plans are carried out must also be recorded. Safety representatives have a right to copies of any documentation that must be kept by statutory requirements. Copies of the plan should therefore be made available to them. Everyone who needs to know what has been decided must get to know about it and they must be made aware about where the plan is kept. This will include: telling the workforce, particularly maintenance workers; telling safety representatives; or preparing packs of information for visiting contractors liable to be at risk.

Guidance

4(8) and (9)

88 The ways in which information is recorded on the whereabouts of ACMs and how they will be managed will vary, but the information needs to be stored in an easily accessible form. For example, using a computer record or storing information via the Internet to record the location and condition of ACMs are two possible ways to do this which can easily be updated.

ACOP

4(8) and (9)

89 If having gone through all the earlier steps in this document it has been decided or discovered that some ACMs in the premises can be left safely in place, arrangements will now need to be made so that information about the location and condition of the ACMs is given to anyone who might disturb them – either accidentally or during the course of their work.

Regulation

4(9)

(9) The measures to be specified in the plan for managing the risk shall include adequate measures for –

(c) ensuring that information about the location and condition of any asbestos or any such substance is –

(i) provided to every person liable to disturb it, and

ACOP

4(9)

90　The arrangements should be written down or recorded in some retrievable and easy to understand way. They should take account of the possibility that the main contact or nominated person may not be there all the time.

Guidance

4(9)

91　One way of doing this is to clearly label, where reasonably practicable, all the ACMs or suspected ACMs on the premises, but the labels will need to be checked from time to time as they may become obscured or fall off. Another way might include a 'permit-to-work' system. For example, anyone who comes to the premises to carry out maintenance work would be required to report to the premises manager or those working in their office. They would issue a pass to this maintenance worker or his/her supervisor to carry out work in a particular part of the premises. At that time they would be provided with all relevant information such as the position and condition of ACMs.

ACOP

4(9)

92　The Management Regulations require that suitable labelling/signs are put in place if there are no other appropriate preventive or protective measures. Labelling should conform with the Health and Safety (Safety Signs and Signals) Regulations 1996.[17]

93　Tell employees what the arrangements are, and provide copies for employee representatives and trade union safety representatives. Remember that this information must be available for all the premises, so if there are separate site managers/building managers responsible for different premises they must each make the information available to those in their respective premises.

94　No-one must work on any ACMs unless the requirements of the Asbestos Regulations are complied with.

Guidance

4(9)

95　Secure arrangements will need to be in place to make sure this happens eg, by telling employees, by putting up notices stating that no building work or maintenance is to be started without written permission, or by using only one contractor who has a copy of the drawing and plan, or using only a contractor who holds a licence from HSE to work on asbestos. Contractors also need to comply with the Asbestos Regulations.

96　There are various ways that the risks can be managed. Here are two examples from opposite ends of the scale. Most situations are likely to lie somewhere in between.

Option 1

97　A 'once and for all' solution could be considered and competent specialists called on to survey all the accessible parts of the premises, analyse any suspect materials and identify the location of any that contain asbestos as set out in MDHS100[8] on Types 2 and 3 surveys.

98　A programme could then be arranged for all the asbestos-containing materials to be removed and replaced with suitable non-asbestos materials. (You will need to assess if there are any risks from substitute materials.) If it is decided to do this, bear in mind that removal can create a risk in itself and during the work the building may not be safe for normal activity.

99　This option can be very costly and it may not be necessary. Also, there are some buildings where it is impossible to remove all of the asbestos without demolishing the building, for example it could be hidden within walls.

Option 2

100   It could be assumed that all the materials that are not recognised in the buildings and fittings in the premises contain asbestos. If this is done, arrangements must be put in place to make sure that no one does any work without being informed that the materials may contain asbestos and taking the necessary precautionary measures detailed in paragraphs 94 and 95. This would also include working close to these materials. This means, in particular, work which would involve cutting, drilling into, sanding or in any way disturbing any of these materials. All the presumed asbestos material would need to be maintained in good condition so that fibres are not released into areas that people use.

101   If option 2 is chosen, and subsequently work needs to be done on the premises, arrangements can be made for the area where the work is going to be done to be surveyed for asbestos and for samples of suspect materials to be analysed. A person who has been accredited for sampling and/or analysis by the United Kingdom Accreditation Service under the international standards BS EN ISO 17025[11] or BS EN ISO 17020[9] as appropriate is likely to be competent to undertake this work. Alternatively a presumption can be made that the material contains asbestos and precautions taken accordingly.

102   If the material is found not to be asbestos, work can go ahead without additional precautions, other than being aware that asbestos-containing materials that were hidden may be made accessible and, if so, suitable action should be taken. If the material is found to contain asbestos, the work must be carried out in accordance with the Control of Asbestos Regulations 2006. The majority of asbestos-containing material removal work will need to be done by a contractor who holds a licence issued by HSE under the Control of Asbestos Regulations 2006. There are a few exceptions to this and details can be found in *Work with materials containing asbestos. Control of Asbestos Regulations 2006. Approved Code of Practice and guidance.*[1]

103   If this option is chosen, a maintenance programme must be in place to ensure that any damage to any part of the premises is identified, the spread or release of debris is immediately prevented and repairs made as soon as is practicable.

104   Although option 2 seems to be the least expensive choice at the beginning, it may turn out to be quite costly and inconvenient in the long term. It is likely, for example, to require further sampling work to identify ACMs before any maintenance work is undertaken.

Middle options

105   Following the inspection, it is worth thinking about alternatives between options 1 and 2. For example:

(a)   Consider using the information on the drawing or record to help decide which parts of the premises might need to be looked at by a specialist surveyor. If parts of the premises are in heavy use and often need repair, or maintenance work is planned, those parts could be surveyed by a specialist and any suspected ACMs sampled to remove any that turn out to be asbestos. Other parts might need only an inspection to identify material that is likely to be asbestos and a check on its condition. A record should be made on the drawing of those parts that have been surveyed.

Guidance

4(9)

(b)   If there are parts of the premises that are not accessible and are not likely to need maintenance, like roof-spaces, ducts or under-floor voids, doing anything more for those places can be put off until it is necessary to have some work done there. However, a note will need to be made on the drawing/record that these areas have not been examined and that they must be presumed to contain ACMs. But make sure that asbestos debris cannot escape from these areas in the meantime and ensure that no one does any work there until an asbestos assessment has been done, and consider having an emergency plan for situations like leaks of water into the areas.

Regulation

4(9)

(9)   *The measures to be specified in the plan for managing the risk shall include adequate measures for –*

(c)   *ensuring that information about the location and condition of any asbestos or any such substance is –*

(ii)   *made available to the emergency services.*

ACOP

4(9)

106 Information on the location and condition of any known, or presumed, ACMs must be made available to the emergency services. The fire services in particular need to be made aware that ACMs are in the premises so that they can take the appropriate precautions in an emergency.

Guidance

4(9)

107 The fire services are the most likely of the emergency services to disturb ACMs or come into contact with disturbed asbestos, so they should be contacted to see what information they want, in what form they would like it, and if they would like the information to be sent to them.

E   *Monitoring arrangements*

Regulation

4(9) and (10)

(9)   *The measures to be specified in the plan for managing the risk shall include adequate measures for –*

(a)   *monitoring the condition of any asbestos or any substance containing or suspected of containing asbestos;*

(10) *The dutyholder shall ensure that –*

(a)   *the plan is reviewed and revised at regular intervals, and forthwith if –*

(i)   *there is reason to suspect that the plan is no longer valid, or*

(ii)   *there has been a significant change in the premises to which the plan relates;*

(b)   *the measures specified in the plan are implemented; and*

(c)   *the measures taken to implement the plan are recorded.*

Guidance

4(9) and (10)

108 Any ACM – identified or suspected – will need to be inspected periodically to check that it has not deteriorated or been damaged. Decisions on how often this needs to be done can be made by thinking about where the material is, how many people work near it, whether it is easy to reach and might get bumped by trolleys or vehicles, whether it might be damaged by vermin or water leakage or whether it is out of the way. It will need to be checked more often if it is in a place where it might get damaged. The records/drawings must be updated to reflect any changes discovered. As a minimum, the material should be checked every six to twelve

months even if it is in good condition and not going to be disturbed, as it may for example be accidentally damaged. The details of the system that will be used to check the condition of the material in the plan must also be written down.

109 Lastly, there should be periodic checks to make sure that the arrangements are working and that people are fully aware of what they should be doing to comply with the duty to manage.

110 How frequently this is checked will depend on how likely the arrangements are to go wrong. Take into account that the more people that need to be involved, the more likely it is that mistakes will be made. Explain what needs to be done to employees and their representatives, so that they can advise if they believe the arrangements are not working properly.

111 The arrangements will need to be reviewed and changes made when eg, new staff are taken on or different sorts of work in the premises are started, or there is a change in the condition of the ACMs. As a minimum, the arrangements should be reviewed every six months even if there have been no changes. The extent of the review will depend upon the size and complexity of the premises. For example, a farmer with an asbestos cement barn in good condition may only need to check that his farm hands know that it contains asbestos and they should not do any (unsupervised) work on it (see *A short guide to managing asbestos in premises*).[14] The details of the review, when it is made, should be written down including whether the arrangements are still satisfactory or whether any changes are made. Everyone who needs to know should be informed of any changes made.

Obligations of contractors

112 Building/maintenance contractors will not take on any direct duties in respect of the duty to manage in regulation 4 (apart from for their own business premises), unless they either have contractual responsibilities for maintenance activities or they exercise some element of control over the site. An example of the latter is where contractors exercise some or full control over part of premises for an extended period, for example where a construction or refurbishment project is 'ring-fenced' from other activities. In such cases, CDM places a clear obligation on the construction client to provide information on asbestos in the premises to the contractor. To clarify their duties the contractor may wish to ensure that the contract specifically excludes 'duty to manage' responsibilities so there is no doubt about their role here. The contractor should be given information on the location and condition of ACMs by the owner or occupier where this will affect their work, so that they can plan and undertake it safely. If a contractor unexpectedly discovers any asbestos or suspected asbestos they must report this to the dutyholder. Also a contractor should tell the dutyholder if there is any discrepancy between the actual condition of the material and the information they are given.

113 If asbestos is likely to be present in the premises, then the contractor will have to comply with regulations 6 and 11 of the Asbestos Regulations, as well as any other health and safety legislation that applies to the work. If the work is known to involve disturbing asbestos, then all of the Asbestos Regulations (apart from regulation 4, which will only apply if the contractor has caretaker duties to manage the risk from asbestos) will apply.

114 Although only the courts can give an authoritative interpretation of the law, in considering the application of these Regulations and guidance to people working under your control and direction who are treated as self-employed for tax and/or National Insurance purposes, they are nevertheless treated as your employees for health and safety purposes. You may therefore need to take

appropriate action to protect them. If you are in any doubt about who is responsible for the health and safety of a person working for you this could be clarified and included in the terms of a contract. However, remember you cannot pass on a legal duty that falls to you under the HSW Act by means of a contract and you will still retain duties towards others by virtue of section 3 of the HSW Act. If you intend to employ such workers on the basis that you are not responsible for their health and safety, you should seek legal advice before doing so.